This book belongs to

....

....

GETTING THE BEST OUT OF MAGICAL ANIMALS

You can get lots of fun out of this book if you act out the stories with friends and family.
If you each take a part in a story, you will soon find it coming to life in front of you.
To add to the fun, turn to page 70 and make your own puppets of your Magical Animals.

MAGICAL ANIMALS

Adapted by Jason Quinn and Sourav Dutta from the original tales.
Illustrated, designed and lettered by Rajesh Nagulakonda.
Activity pages created by Kate Tompsett, designed by Era Chawla.
Desktop publishing by Bhavnath Chaudhary.

Mission Statement

To entertain and educate young minds by creating unique illustrated books
that recount stories of human values, arouse curiosity in the world around us,
and inspire with tales of great deeds of unforgettable people.

Published by Kalyani Navyug Media Pvt Ltd
101 C, Shiv House, Hari Nagar Ashram,
New Delhi 110014, India
ISBN: 978-93-80741-84-0

Printed in India

Magical Animals

KALYANI NAVYUG MEDIA PVT LTD

NEW DELHI

Goldilocks and
the Three Bears

Once upon a time, in the village of Ever-After, there lived a little girl called Goldilocks. She liked playing with her dolls all day long.

Goldilocks' Mummy was always busy. She swept the floors...

...milked the cows...

...and cooked all the meals.

Goldilocks never helped her Mummy.

"Goldilocks, can you help me please?"

"What does Mummy want, now?"

"Goldilocks, will you go to the shop and buy some bread and sugar?"

"But I want to play with my dolls…"

It's not fair. I want to play.

I don't want to go to the silly old shop.

Goldilocks was lazy and she did not like helping anyone.

On the way, Goldilocks met her best friend, Red Riding Hood.

Hi, Goldilocks!

Do you want to play?

I can't. I have to visit my Grandma.

Bye, Goldilocks!

Red Riding Hood's Grandma makes lovely cakes and ice cream.

Mummy can wait for her bread and sugar. I'm going to have some ice cream.

Hey! Wait for me, Red Riding Hood!

Red Riding Hood! Where are you?

I am so thirsty!

Goldilocks reached a little pond.

Oh goody! I can have a drink at last.

But before she could drink...

EWW! YUCK!

The water's lovely, have a drink. It will do you good, I think.

I'm not drinking a smelly frog's dirty bath water.

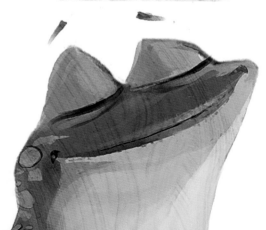

Soon Goldilocks saw a pretty, little cottage.

Maybe I can get some water here.

KNOCK

KNOCK

Nobody answered the door, so Goldilocks went inside.

CREEEAK

Goldilocks was very hungry, and there were three bowls of porridge on the table.

I'll have a little taste. Nobody will ever know.

But the porridge in the big bowl was too hot for poor Goldilocks.

PTOOO!

So she tried the porridge in the smaller bowl.

But the porridge in this bowl was too cold.

YUCK!

Goldilocks decided to taste the porridge in the tiny bowl.

This had better be good.

This is not too hot and not too cold. It's just perfect.

When Goldilocks had finished eating, she felt sleepy.

I think I will just sit down and rest a little.

YAWN!

Goldilocks decided to explore the rest of the cottage.

Wow!

Look at these beds. I wonder who sleeps here.

YAAWN!

I feel sleepy...

Goldilocks wanted to lie on the **big bed.**

This bed is too high and hard for me.

Then Goldilocks tried the smaller bed.

This bed is too soft for me.

At last Goldilocks got into the **tiny bed.**

This bed is so comfy. It's just perfect.

Soon, the owners of the cottage returned from their morning walk.

Come on, Daddy, I'm starving!

Me too, son.

Let's have breakfast.

That's funny. Someone's been sitting on my chair.

That's funny. Someone's been sitting on my chair too.

Someone's been sitting on my chair too, and it's broken! Not funny!

Don't worry, I'll make you a new one.

... she's still sleeping in it!

Huh?
What's all that noise?

HELP!

Poor Goldilocks was so frightened that she ran out of the cottage...

MUMMY!

24

...and she did not stop running...

...until she reached the shop.

Bread and sugar, please.

When Goldilocks reached home, she told Mummy the whole story.

You have been a very naughty girl. We shall go to the Bears tomorrow and give them a big pot of porridge.

From that day on, Goldilocks always listened to her Mummy.

The Three Little Pigs

Once upon a time, there was a family of Pigs.
They lived on the edge of the village of Ever-After.

Mummy Pig knew it was time for her children to grow up,
so she sent them out into the world to look after themselves.

Remember, children, if a job is worth doing at all...

...it's worth doing well.

The Three Little Pigs decided to build themselves new houses to live in.

I'm going to build my house out of straw.

Straw?

Yes, straw. It's easy. I made one in school.

Just because it's easy doesn't mean it's good.

It will blow away in the wind.

You are just jealous. Leave me alone!

The Second Little Pig and the Third Little Pig had their own plans.

I will make my house with twigs. It will be quick to make, and better than First Pig's house.

Yes, but not the best.

I will make my house with bricks. It will take a lot of time and hard work, but it will be a strong house.

Soon, the First Little Pig made his house of straw.

Hey! That straw is mine!

That night, as the First Little Pig sat all by himself...

I wonder what my brothers are doing.

KNOCK!

KNOCK!

?!

....he had a visitor.

Little Pig! Little Pig! Let me come in!

It was the Big Bad Wolf!

NO!

I won't let you come in. Not by the hair on my chinny-chin-chin.

Then I'll

Huff...

And I'll

Puff...

And I'll blow your house down!

EEK!
Mummy!

The First Little Pig ran away as fast as he could.

Hey! Come back!

The next morning, the Second Little Pig had just finished making his house out of twigs.

♪♪ There's no place like home.

Hmm! This is so nice! And it was so easy to make.

Hey! There was a Big Bad Wolf, and he huffed, and he puffed...

...and he blew my house down!

Can I stay with you? Please?

Of course, you can.

It's all your own fault for making a house of straw. Remember, if a job's worth doing at all...

It's worth doing well.

KNOCK!

KNOCK!

Who is it?

May be it's the Big Bad Wolf.

YES!

Little Pigs! Little Pigs! Let me come in!

NO!

We won't let you come in. Not by the hair on our chinny-chin-chins.

Then I'll **Huff...**

And I'll **Puff...**

The Third Little Pig made his house out of bricks.

There, all finished.

Help us!

There was a Big Bad Wolf...

...and he huffed, and he puffed, and he blew our houses down.

Ha! I'll climb down the chimney and gobble them all up.

Little Pigs! Little Pigs!

Let me come in!

Now he'll eat us.

No. Roll that barrel into the fireplace.

The barrel?

Into the fireplace?

Just help me.
You will see why.

Perfect!
Now just wait.

I don't see how that's going to save us.

I'm coming to get you!

I'm too young to be eaten.

Me too.

43

THUD

Hooray! We trapped the Big Bad Wolf!

The Three Little Pigs rolled the barrel out of the house.

HELP!

YIPPEE!

The barrel rolled all the way down the hill.

SPLASH

The Big Bad Wolf never bothered the Three Little Pigs again.

Poor old Wolf, he's so wet. He hasn't had his dinner yet.

45

The Little Pigs had learned an important lesson...

...If a job's worth doing at all… It's worth doing well.

The Frog Prince

It's so boring being a slimy frog. I wish I was a pig, or a bear, or a dog.

What's that song that I can hear? Someone's coming, coming near.

Well, well, well; It's the lovely Princess Annabelle!

When, O when, as my dream foretold; Shall I meet a prince all dashing and bold?

She's so beautiful, and she's so sweet; From the crown of her head to the toes of her feet.

OOOPS!

SPLASH

Oh no, my golden ball. It's lost forever!

Why so gloomy, why so sad? What can I do to make you glad?

I have lost my ball. Can you help me?

Please don't worry. I can get your ball, If you grant me a wish that is quite small.

A wish?

I am the Princess. You **have to** help me.

Listen Princess, grant me one wish; Or your ball will stay lost with the frogs and the fish.

Oh well, tell me what you want.

SSSFFRRRAAKKK

Eeeek!

♪ Be my friend and take me to your home; I don't like living out here on my own.

♪ Let me eat off your own plate;
And give me a kiss when it's getting late.

Fine, I promise.
Now get me my ball.

SPLASH

Your golden ball I did save;
Remember the promise
that you gave.

Promise? What
promise?

Goodbye,
little frog.

TEE-HEE-HEE

I'll tell you
this, my royal
friend,
I'll get what
I want in
the end.

All day long, the frog hopped along, as he followed in Princess Annabelle's footsteps.

Later that evening...

KNOCK!
KNOCK!

Who's there?

Evening, sweetheart, I hope I'm not late. I'm starving so take me to your plate.

And the frog told the King his tale of how the Princess did not keep her promise.

Annabelle, you must always keep your promises.

But...

No buts.

It's late, shouldn't you be going home?

Buuuurrp

But you promised me that I could stay; Would you break your word and send me away?

Remember, dear, a promise is a promise.

Yes, Father.

59

Remember your promise, little Miss; You promised to give me a goodnight kiss.

I'd rather **NOT!!**

PROMISES... PROMISES... PROMISES...

AAAAIAIEEEE!!

He shoots, and he scores!

Good shot!

'We didn't know it, but we were in front of the cottage of an evil witch.'

CRAASSHHH

Who dares disturb me at my spell? Speak, my child, speak and tell.

You've been wicked, you've been bad, you've made me really, really mad.

Awww...
Do not be sad,
you break my heart!
A kiss from a princess will
free you from my art.

Please have mercy,
can't you see?
Would any princess
ever kiss me?

But I was
wrong, you saved
me. Thank you
very much!

Annabelle had learned her lesson. She never broke a promise again.

When her birthday came, she invited everyone from this book.

SOCK IT TO ME!

Now's your chance to have fun with these cute Magical Animal sock puppets!

You Will Need:

- Green, brown and pink socks
- PVA glue and glue brush
- paints and paintbrush
- brown, beige, dark and light pink, green, white and black felt fabric
- cereal box card
- scissors
- pencil
- cotton wool balls

MAKING ONE OF THE LITTLE PIGS!

STEP 1

To start, fold a piece of cereal box card in half. Draw a half oval shape onto it, and cut it out.

STEP 2

Glue the card shape onto some black felt, and cut around the edge. This is going to be your piggy's mouth!

STEP 3

Cut off the toe end of a pink sock.

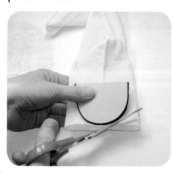

Place the folded black mouth on the edge of the sock, and cut around it. Open out the sock and glue the mouth inside it. Only glue around the outside edge of the mouth, so that you can still get your hand inside. Tuck any loose edges inside as you glue.

Cut out and stick on pink ears, black eyes and a pink nose.

Get ready to play!

Making your other animal friends is just as easy!

TO MAKE THE FROG PRINCE:

Use a green sock, and make a red diamond-shaped mouth with a pink tongue. Glue a ball of cotton wool to white felt and glue into a ball. Wrap some green felt around it to make an eyelid, and add a black felt circle to the middle. Make a second eye in the same way, and glue these onto the sock. Roll some yellow felt into a tube and cut into a crown shape. Now glue the crown onto your Frog Prince!

TO MAKE THE BIG BAD WOLF:

You will need a brown or black sock for Wolfy! Cut out a long oval shape from card and cover it in black felt. Glue on a piece of red felt for his tongue. Cut eyes from yellow and black felt, and add beige and brown felt ears, and black eyebrows. Wrap a ball of cotton wool in black felt to make a nose, and glue it into place. You can make his teeth by cutting triangular shapes of white felt.

Now you're ready to play!

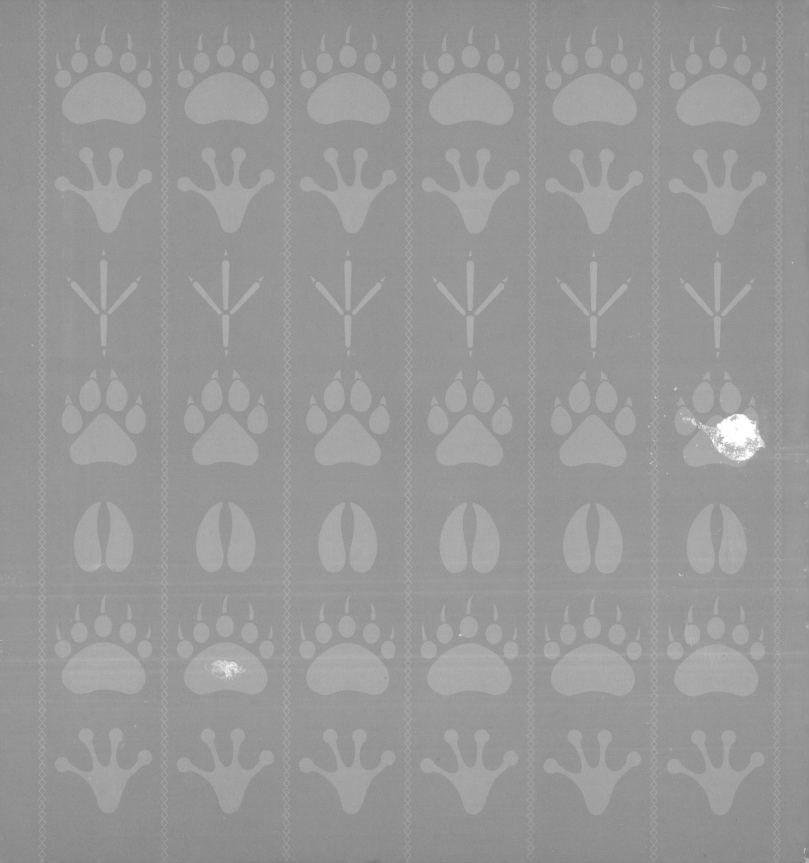

Colour the Frog Prince nice and bright,
And make this scene a pretty sight.